WARNING!

This book is intended for adults who wish to maintain and inspire their great relationship. Also, the author is in no way medically trained and readers should consult with their doctor to ensure that they are healthy enough to have sex. Some of the situations and activities may be illegal and the readers should be aware of his/her state laws.

ADULT CONTENT

Add us on Facebook!

VISIT OUR WEBSITE
www.SexBucketList.com

Printed in the United States of America
Second Edition: 2016
Book Concept & Author: Michael Lucente
Cover Photography: Shawn Miller
Design & Illustration: Shawn Miller and Curtis Doll III
Portrait Photography: DJ Woodard / DJwoodard.com

INSTRUCTIONS

NAME OF LOVER

_____

NAME OF LOVER

_____

▶▶▶ THIS BOOK WAS FIRST OPENED ON ◀◀◀

__ / __ / ____

STAMP THIS
WHEN
COMPLETED

DO IT!

| PAGE CHALLENGE | DATE: |

YES! IT'S THAT EASY! AFTER YOU AND YOUR
LOVER HAVE READ THESE INSTRUCTIONS........
SEE! YOUR FIRST PAGE CHALLENGE IS DONE!

STAMP THIS
WHEN
COMPLETED

DO IT!

| DATE: |

TABLE OF CONTENTS

First and foremost, you need to HAVE FUN!
But why have a bucket list at all?
Or more importantly, why have a Sex Bucket List?

The Sex Bucket List® is important for many reasons. You wouldn't go to the grocery store without a grocery list, would you? And it's pretty challenging to make that new dinner recipe without the list of ingredients, right? Well the same goes for your sex life. How would you know if you're missing out on something? You may never have thought of this element or even tried that… Or, if you're like me, you might take this recipe for life and find a way to make it better, or more suitable for you and your Busy Buddy.

This is why I created **The Sex Bucket List**®. It's here to push you to be more adventurous and spontaneous. It's here to rid you of the routine sex. Don't get me wrong, there is nothing wrong with Sunday morning doggie style. But if that is the only action you and your lover get all week, there's a problem.

This new adventure you are about to embark upon will be exactly that. This is not about the crazy things you did when you were young, or maybe even last week. The sextivities to follow are for right now and going forward. A clean slate, fresh start, whatever you want to call it. Sure, you may have done a few of the 600-plus sextivities within this book already. Well, guess what? You get to do them again. Shucks, right? I know. But you make the rules, not me. Stamp off what you've done in the past if you like, just make sure it was with your current partner. Also, try to aim for multiple stamps each time you Get Busy. It's a lot of fun this way.

 Now take the kiss stamper and start stamping and dating sextivities completed from this day forward. The first one on the list is "While Stamping this Book."

GET BUSY, GETTIN' BUSY!

KEEPING CREATIVE

CREATIVE SEX > ROUTINE SEX

Your sex life can often become just like your work life. Stay with me here. At first you're crazy excited to get started, get down-n-dirty, and just make things happen. Then you discover you can slack a little in this area or even skip this part completely. Then you get to the point that you're just going through the motions day after day, and giving just enough effort to get through yet another routine day. If you act now, you can be like Forny and Kate, hanging out and *Gettin' Busy* like rabbits and loving every minute of it.

So to keep the creative juices flowing at all times there are some things you'll have to know and do. You have to know upfront what you and your partner will and will not do. You have to know the hard no's and the soft no's and make sure you are actually listening when you have this conversation. You need to find a way to hang out together more.

This doesn't have to be a week-long vacation or even a weekend trip. Just go out and do something together. Get out of the house for an hour and have some fun. If you can't think of something to do, fear not, there's a fun list to come. But if you routinely sit on the couch and have to wait until your favorite TV show is over before you even think about *Gettin' Busy* you've already fallen into a poor routine. But hey, if that is your thing, try this. Instead of fast forwarding through the commercials why not try to start and finish before the show starts and the commercials are over? That should make for a good one in the **"PERSONALS"** section!

THE POWER OF TWO!

IT'S YOUR SEX LIFE... SO ENJOY IT!

Yes, I wrote this book, but it's your **Sex Bucket List**® now. You get to make the rules. Don't read too deep into the sextivities soon to follow. And you don't have to be specific or precise. If you and your Busy Buddy have no intention to visit Antarctica whatsoever, then don't! Pop in a documentary and stamp it off that way. It's cool, you make the rules.

There is an entire section dedicated to you. The "PERSONALS" section is specifically for you and your sexy partner. This section is for any *sextivities* I have not included. Whether it be a hobby, a specific date, a trip you went on, or just because you farted mid-thrust! LOL! But also keep track of first times and tenth times here. You can make a list of new fetishes you experimented with. Again, it's your sex life. This is now your copy of **The Sex Bucket List**®. Enjoy it the way you want it. List your favorite and not-so-favorite role-playing scenarios here as well.

 IF YOU DIDN'T ENJOY IT, TURN THE KISS STAMPER UPSIDE-DOWN WHEN COMPLETED.

I WANT TO WISH YOU AND YOUR LOVE THE BEST.
I HOPE THE SEX BUCKET LIST BRINGS YOU HOURS OF FUN AT A TIME.

 Feel free to share all of your triumphs on our Facebook Page!

www.Facebook.com/SEXbucketlist®

THANKS AGAIN AND AS ALWAYS...
GET BUSY, GETTIN' BUSY!
MICHAEL LUCENTE

DRAW & WRITE NOTES FOR YOUR LOVER, CIRCLE BODY PARTS THAT GET YOU HOT !

SEX BUCKET LIST®

- WHILE STAMPING THIS BOOK — DATE:
- BIRDS CHIRPING — DATE:
- HANDCUFFS — DATE:
- WAKE UP YOUR LOVER TO IT — DATE:
- WITH A TOY — DATE:
- MIDDLE OF AN ARGUMENT — DATE:
- WITH FRUIT — DATE:
- FRESH OUT OF THE SHOWER — DATE:
- BOTTLE OF WINE — DATE:
- SIDE OF THE ROAD — DATE:

PAGE CHALLENGE) DATE:

MAKIN' IT OBVIOUS! HAVE A LOUD QUICKIE IN A CHANGING ROOM. SLAP A HIGH FIVE WHEN YOU GET OUT WHILE EVERYONE IS EYEBALLING YOU.

ROLE-PLAYING) DATE:

CANDLE LIGHT) DATE:

WITH A HEADACHE) DATE:

WHILE READING THIS BOOK) DATE:

GENTLE) DATE:

ROUGH) DATE:

WOKEN UP TO IT) DATE:

TIED UP) DATE:

ACTING LIKE ANIMALS) DATE:

LATE TO WORK BECAUSE OF IT) DATE:

SEX BUCKET LIST®

EXCLUSIVES

CHANGING ROOM   DATE:

TO CELEBRATE   DATE:

WHIP CREAM   DATE:

ON BUBBLE WRAP   DATE:

IN PUBLIC   DATE:

HISTORIC MARKER   DATE:

DANCE FLOOR   DATE:

BOUNCE HOUSE   DATE:

MIRROR MAZE   DATE:

ON TOP OF THE SBL BOOK   DATE:

7

PAGE CHALLENGE DATE:

WHILE PLAYING AS A NURSE OR DOCTOR, USE THE SEX BUCKET LIST AS A PATIENT CHART AND GIVE YOUR PATIENT WHAT IS NEEDED.

STANLEY CUP DATE:

ON A MONSTER TRUCK DATE:

ON A RIDING LAWNMOWER DATE:

SKY DIVING DATE:

OUTER SPACE DATE:

AT AN ADULT RETREAT DATE:

GIVING A MASSAGE DATE:

HIGH-FIVING DATE:

LOUD DATE:

MULTIPLE ORGASMS DATE:

SOMETHING THAT'S...

BLACK — DATE:

WHITE — DATE:

BLUE — DATE:

GREEN — DATE:

GRAY — DATE:

BROWN — DATE:

ORANGE — DATE:

RED — DATE:

PURPLE — DATE:

PINK — DATE:

9

WHAT'S BLACK AND WHITE WITH RED ALL OVER? WHERE WE JUST GOT BUSY!

YELLOW) DATE:

HARD) DATE:

SOFT) DATE:

SHINY) DATE:

DULL) DATE:

SPARKLY) DATE:

WET) DATE:

DRY) DATE:

ROUND) DATE:

SQUARE) DATE:

SOMETHING THAT'S...

RECTANGULAR — DATE:

TRIANGULAR — DATE:

CYLINDRICAL — DATE:

CARPET — DATE:

VINYL — DATE:

WOOD — DATE:

MARBLE — DATE:

CERAMIC — DATE:

SHABBY — DATE:

RADIANT — DATE:

PAGE CHALLENGE   DATE:

TRY GETTIN' BUSY IN A FANCY ELEVATOR WITH A SHINY MARBLE FLOOR AND GLASS WALLS. THAT'LL GIVE'EM SOMETHING TO TALK ABOUT!

DELICATE   DATE:

BRITTLE   DATE:

TRANSPARENT   DATE:

ARTIFICIAL   DATE:

ORGANIC   DATE:

STEEP   DATE:

FLAT   DATE:

REFLECTIVE   DATE:

SPONGY   DATE:

BOUNCY   DATE:

DURING OR WHILE...

GETTING READY FOR BED DATE:

WEDDING PARTY DATE:

CLEANING DATE:

BORED DATE:

GETTING READY FOR WORK DATE:

RADIO ON DATE:

EATING DATE:

UNDER BLANKETS DATE:

WATCHING TV DATE:

ON VACATION DATE:

PAGE CHALLENGE   DATE:

HOP ON THE JOGGING TRAIL AND SCOUT OUT
A NICE PLACE TO DIP OFF AND GET BUSY.
MAKE SURE TO CHECK FOR TICKS AFTER!

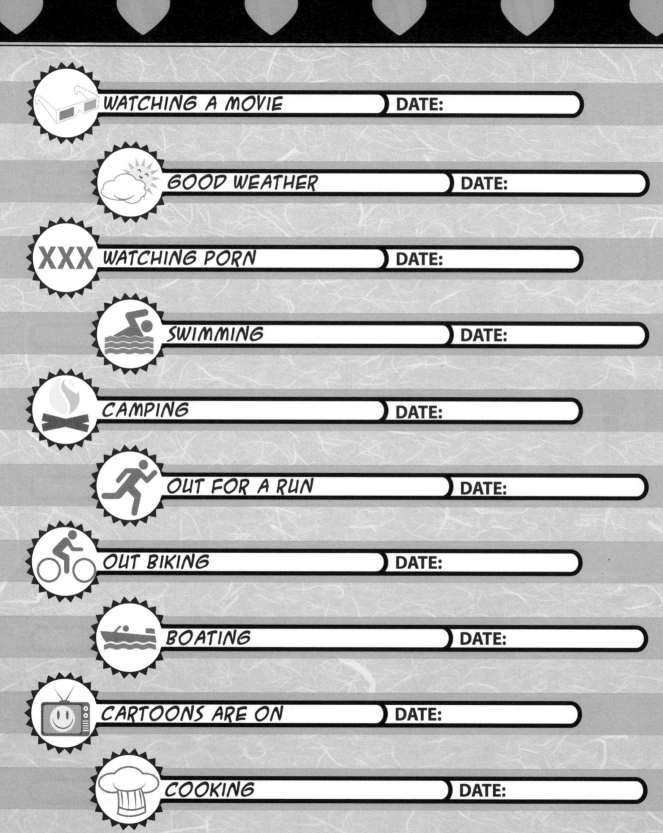

WATCHING A MOVIE   DATE:

GOOD WEATHER   DATE:

WATCHING PORN   DATE:

SWIMMING   DATE:

CAMPING   DATE:

OUT FOR A RUN   DATE:

OUT BIKING   DATE:

BOATING   DATE:

CARTOONS ARE ON   DATE:

COOKING   DATE:

DURING OR WHILE...

READING — DATE:

PLAYING VIDEO GAMES — DATE:

PLAYING A BOARD GAME — DATE:

LYING DOWN — DATE:

STANDING — DATE:

SITTING — DATE:

MAKING A DRINK — DATE:

SOBER — DATE:

DRUNK — DATE:

LOOKING IN THE MIRROR — DATE:

PAGE CHALLENGE   DATE:

ON A MUSEUM TOUR, SNEAK OFF TO A QUIET PLACE + MAKE YOUR OWN ATTRACTION. LOCATE WHERE YOU ARE ON THE MAP AND STAMP IT!

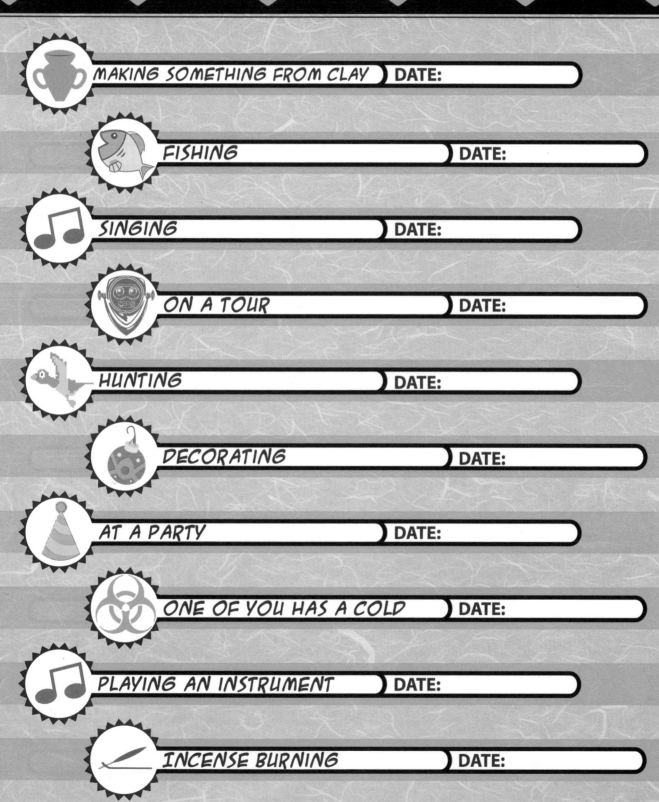

MAKING SOMETHING FROM CLAY   DATE:

FISHING   DATE:

SINGING   DATE:

ON A TOUR   DATE:

HUNTING   DATE:

DECORATING   DATE:

AT A PARTY   DATE:

ONE OF YOU HAS A COLD   DATE:

PLAYING AN INSTRUMENT   DATE:

INCENSE BURNING   DATE:

DURING OR WHILE...

TORNADO SIREN GOING OFF) DATE:

IT IS PAYDAY) DATE:

THE NEWS IS ON) DATE:

SUN BURNT) DATE:

WINDY DAY) DATE:

SUNSET) DATE:

SUNRISE) DATE:

STARING AT CLOUDS) DATE:

UNDER A TREE) DATE:

ON THE PHONE) DATE:

PAGE CHALLENGE

DATE:

GET THEM BEADS!
SNEAK ON TO A MARDI GRAS FLOAT...
OR JUST DO IT RIGHT OUT IN THE OPEN.

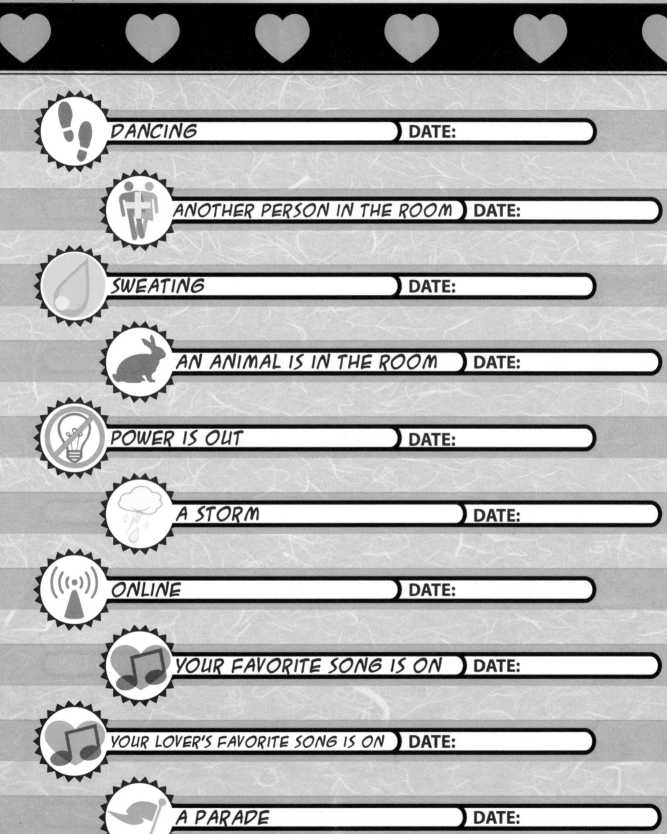

DANCING **DATE:**

ANOTHER PERSON IN THE ROOM **DATE:**

SWEATING **DATE:**

AN ANIMAL IS IN THE ROOM **DATE:**

POWER IS OUT **DATE:**

A STORM **DATE:**

ONLINE **DATE:**

YOUR FAVORITE SONG IS ON **DATE:**

YOUR LOVER'S FAVORITE SONG IS ON **DATE:**

A PARADE **DATE:**

ON OR AGAINST...

COUCH DATE:

TOWEL DATE:

BED DATE:

BLANKETS DATE:

REFRIGERATOR DATE:

STAIRS DATE:

THE FLOOR DATE:

COUNTER DATE:

HEADSTONE DATE:

CHAIR DATE:

MOVE FROM A COUCH TO THE FLOOR IN A STAGED ROOM AT A HOME FURNISHING STORE. "EVERYTHING YOU NEED TO GET BUSY IN ONE PLACE!"

RECLINER) DATE:

TABLE) DATE:

BREAKFAST TABLE) DATE:

DINNER TABLE) DATE:

OTTOMAN) DATE:

RUG) DATE:

DESK) DATE:

EXERCISE EQUIPMENT) DATE:

PILLOW) DATE:

CAPTAIN'S CHAIR) DATE:

ON OR AGAINST...

OFFICE CHAIR — DATE:

WASHING MACHINE — DATE:

DRYER — DATE:

THE WALL — DATE:

PATIO FURNITURE — DATE:

INNER TUBE — DATE:

TRAMPOLINE — DATE:

BENCH — DATE:

PICNIC TABLE — DATE:

WATERBED — DATE:

PAGE CHALLENGE) **DATE:**

FLOATING SEX UNDER THE STARS! ON A WARM STARRY NIGHT, TIE THE INNER TUBE TO THE DOCK, HOP ON, AND GET CLOSE, REAL CLOSE.

DOCK) DATE:

COT) DATE:

FENCE) DATE:

DOOR) DATE:

TOOL BENCH) DATE:

WHEELCHAIR) DATE:

FLAG POLE) DATE:

CHAISE LOUNGE) DATE:

LOVE SEAT) DATE:

ELEVATOR) DATE:

ON OR AGAINST...

BUNK BEDS   DATE:

STEPSTOOL   DATE:

LADDER   DATE:

AIR MATTRESS   DATE:

SLEEPING BAG   DATE:

PILE OF MONEY   DATE:

FLOWER PETALS   DATE:

A SAFE   DATE:

PLASTIC   DATE:

WOOD   DATE:

SAFE SEX! TRY MAKING A QUICK DEPOSIT WHILE CHECKING YOUR SAFETY DEPOSIT BOX IN THE SAFE AT YOUR BANK.

METAL   (**DATE:**)

WOOL   (**DATE:**)

LEATHER   (**DATE:**)

SILK   (**DATE:**)

SATIN   (**DATE:**)

LACE   (**DATE:**)

HAYSTACK   (**DATE:**)

BALCONY   (**DATE:**)

DIVING BOARD   (**DATE:**)

CONCRETE   (**DATE:**)

AFTER

DINNER | DATE:

A SHOWER | DATE:

LUNCH | DATE:

GIFTING THE SEX BUCKET LIST | DATE:

BREAKFAST | DATE:

TELLING A FRIEND ABOUT SBL | DATE:

A NIGHT ON THE TOWN | DATE:

BALLET | DATE:

OPERA | DATE:

A PLAY | DATE:

LET EVERYONE YOU'RE OUT WITH KNOW YOU'RE HEADING HOME TO STAMP OFF A DOUBLE HEADER IN THE SEX BUCKET LIST®... THEN GO DO IT!

A MOVIE DATE:

A VACATION DATE:

A ROAD TRIP DATE:

GETTIN' BUSY DATE:

WORK DATE:

PUTTING KIDS TO BED DATE:

A SPORTING EVENT DATE:

DESSERT DATE:

PLANE FLIGHT DATE:

A PARTY DATE:

AFTER

A WALK — DATE:

A RUN — DATE:

BIKING — DATE:

A SUNSET — DATE:

A SUNRISE — DATE:

AN ARGUMENT — DATE:

TICKLING EACH OTHER — DATE:

WRESTLING EACH OTER — DATE:

A PILLOW FIGHT — DATE:

WALKING IN THE DOOR — DATE:

PAGE CHALLENGE   DATE:

TAKE AN EVENING WALK, WATCH THE SUNSET TO COOL DOWN + AS YOU GET COLD WITHOUT THE SUN AROUND, GET BUSY TO WARM THINGS BACK UP!

WALKING THE DOG   DATE:

YOU BOTH WAKE UP   DATE:

GOING TO THE CIRCUS   DATE:

CHINESE FOOD   DATE:

SUSHI   DATE:

GOING TO A STRIP CLUB   DATE:

AN ASSEMBLY   DATE:

A CONCERT   DATE:

WORKING OUT   DATE:

BATH   DATE:

PAINTING A ROOM — DATE:

DINNER WITH THE PARENTS — DATE:

CHURCH — DATE:

SHOPPING — DATE:

OPENING A GIFT — DATE:

OPENING THE SEX BUCKET LIST — DATE:

SIX-WEEK POSTPARTUM CHECKUP — DATE:

FOREPLAY — DATE:

HANGING UP ON A TELEMARKETER — DATE:

VOTING — DATE:

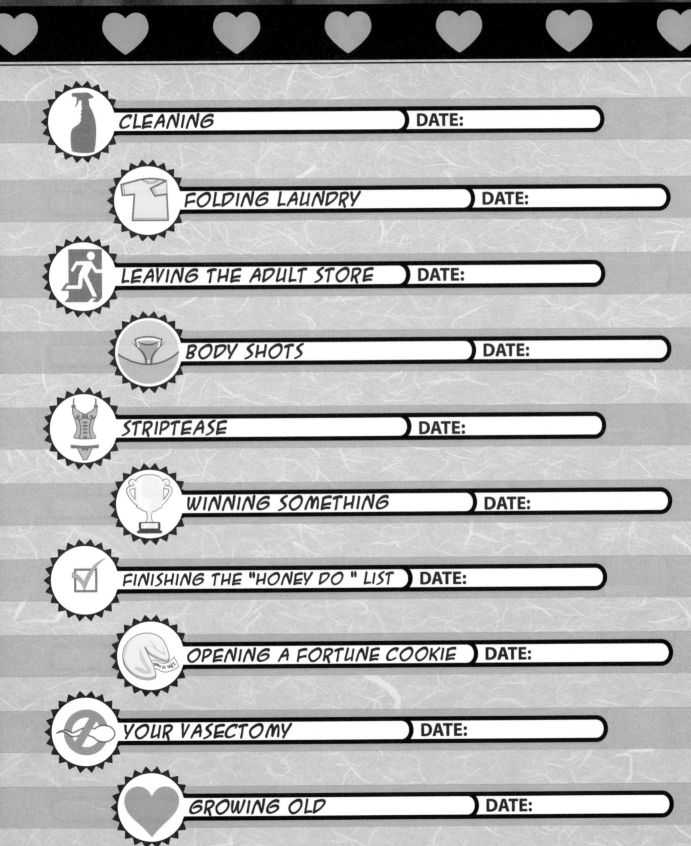

CLEANING) DATE:

FOLDING LAUNDRY) DATE:

LEAVING THE ADULT STORE) DATE:

BODY SHOTS) DATE:

STRIPTEASE) DATE:

WINNING SOMETHING) DATE:

FINISHING THE "HONEY DO " LIST) DATE:

OPENING A FORTUNE COOKIE) DATE:

YOUR VASECTOMY) DATE:

GROWING OLD) DATE:

APPAREL

FULLY CLOTHED) DATE:

NAKED) DATE:

SOCKS ONLY) DATE:

SHOES ONLY) DATE:

BATHING SUITS) DATE:

COWBOY) DATE:

COWGIRL HAT) DATE:

LINGERIE) DATE:

IN COSTUMES) DATE:

DRESS) DATE:

PAGE CHALLENGE   DATE:

WEAR COSTUMES ON A DAY YOU WOULD HAVE
NO REASON TO WEAR THEM...
..OTHER THAN TO STAMP IT OFF.

SKIRT   DATE:

SHIRTS ON   DATE:

PANTS ON   DATE:

PANTS AT ANKLES   DATE:

ONLY ONE OF YOU NAKED   DATE:

UNDERWEAR   DATE:

HOOKER BOOTS   DATE:

HIGH HEELS   DATE:

HAT   DATE:

CROTCHLESS   DATE:

ROOMS

EACH ROOM IN THE HOUSE) DATE:

EACH KID'S ROOM) DATE:

KITCHEN) DATE:

BATHROOM) DATE:

BEDROOM 1) DATE:

BEDROOM 2) DATE:

BEDROOM 3) DATE:

BEDROOM 4) DATE:

LAUNDRY ROOM) DATE:

DINING ROOM) DATE:

LIVING ROOM   DATE:

RECREATION ROOM   DATE:

DEN   DATE:

GARAGE   DATE:

FOYER   DATE:

HALLWAY   DATE:

IN A DOORWAY   DATE:

BEDROOM CLOSET   DATE:

COMPUTER ROOM   DATE:

OFFICE   DATE:

ROOMS

STUDY — DATE:

START IN ONE ROOM + FINISH IN ANOTHER — DATE:

GAME ROOM — DATE:

ATTIC — DATE:

LIBRARY — DATE:

BASEMENT — DATE:

BOUDOIR — DATE:

CELLAR — DATE:

CONSERVATORY — DATE:

NURSERY — DATE:

WHIPS + CHAINS + LEATHER... OH MY! STAGE A ROOM
TO LOOK LIKE A DUNGEON.
DON'T FORGET YOUR SAFE WORD!

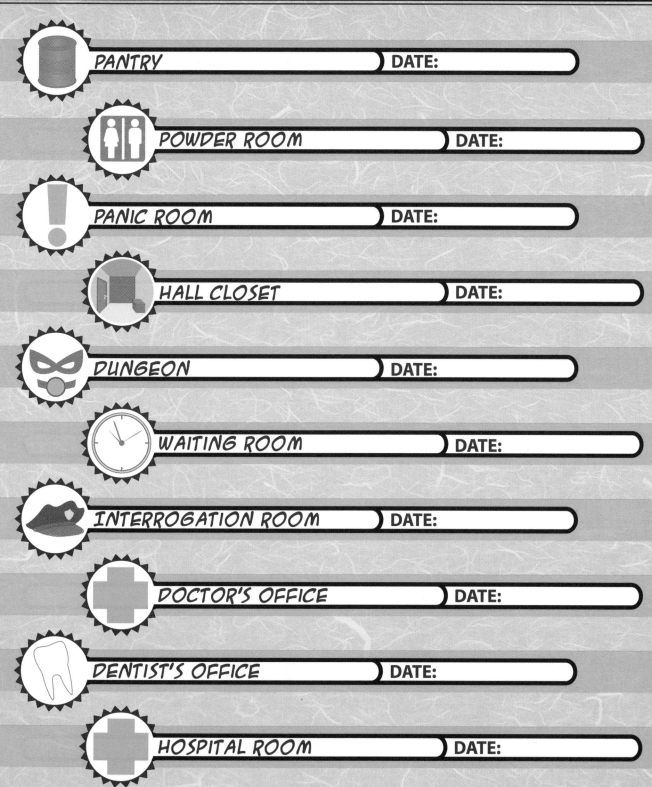

PANTRY   DATE:

POWDER ROOM   DATE:

PANIC ROOM   DATE:

HALL CLOSET   DATE:

DUNGEON   DATE:

WAITING ROOM   DATE:

INTERROGATION ROOM   DATE:

DOCTOR'S OFFICE   DATE:

DENTIST'S OFFICE   DATE:

HOSPITAL ROOM   DATE:

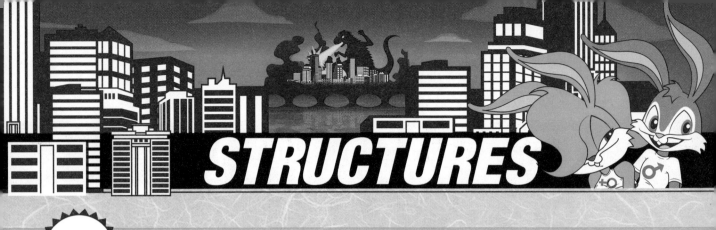

STRUCTURES

HOTEL — DATE:

MOTEL — DATE:

PARKING GARAGE — DATE:

FARM — DATE:

STORE — DATE:

HUT — DATE:

PARK — DATE:

CABIN — DATE:

HOUSE — DATE:

YOUR PARENTS' HOUSE — DATE:

GET BUSY ON ANY RIDE AT A THEME PARK.
SMILE FOR THE COASTER CAM!

YOUR LOVER'S PARENTS' HOUSE   DATE:

GAS STATION   DATE:

YOUR WORK   DATE:

YOUR LOVER'S WORK   DATE:

A BRIDGE   DATE:

ON A ROOF   DATE:

STAIRWELL   DATE:

THEME PARK   DATE:

RESORT   DATE:

RECEPTION HALL   DATE:

STRUCTURES

GYM — DATE:

TENT — DATE:

MOVIE THEATHER — DATE:

IN A BOX — DATE:

SWING — DATE:

TEPEE — DATE:

HOSPITAL — DATE:

IGLOO — DATE:

PLAYGROUND — DATE:

WATER TOWER — DATE:

PAGE CHALLENGE ⟩ DATE:

TOGETHER, BUILD AN IGLOO IN THE SNOW AND GET INSIDE TILL THE TWO OF YOU MELT IT DOWN!

BILLBOARD ⟩ DATE:

RESTAURANT ⟩ DATE:

LIBRARY ⟩ DATE:

LIGHTHOUSE ⟩ DATE:

A REST STOP ⟩ DATE:

A CAVE ⟩ DATE:

A TREEHOUSE ⟩ DATE:

SOMEONE ELSE'S HOME ⟩ DATE:

CHURCH ⟩ DATE:

FUNERAL HOME ⟩ DATE:

TRANSPORTATION

CAR — DATE:

RENTAL CAR — DATE:

HOT AIR BALLOON — DATE:

JET SKI — DATE:

BOAT — DATE:

LIMO — DATE:

PLANE — DATE:

CANOE — DATE:

MOTORCYCLE — DATE:

CAMPER — DATE:

PAGE CHALLENGE | DATE:

TRY STANDING IN A LIMO WITH YOUR HEAD OUT THE SUNROOF. "WELCOME TO AMERICA!"

MOTORHOME | DATE:

VAN | DATE:

CRUISE SHIP | DATE:

TRAIN | DATE:

BUS | DATE:

RAFT | DATE:

SUV | DATE:

TANK | DATE:

HELICOPTER | DATE:

SUBMARINE | DATE:

TRANSPORTATION

CAB OR TAXI   DATE:

BIKE   DATE:

SKATEBOARD   DATE:

POWER SCOOTER   DATE:

ROCKET SHIP   DATE:

TROLLEY   DATE:

SEMITRUCK   DATE:

SEGWAY   DATE:

AMBULANCE   DATE:

FIRE TRUCK   DATE:

43

PAGE CHALLENGE) DATE:

ON A BED, IN A MOVING TRUCK WHILE ON THE ROAD.
GETTIN' BUSY GETTIN' THERE!

MOVING TRUCK) DATE:

ATV) DATE:

FORKLIFT) DATE:

SAILBOAT) DATE:

MUSCLE CAR) DATE:

CLASSIC CAR) DATE:

MOPED) DATE:

SKYWAY) DATE:

AIRBOAT) DATE:

TRAILER) DATE:

OUTDOORS

IN THE FOREST — DATE:

SCENIC OVERLOOK — DATE:

IN A JUNGLE — DATE:

GRAVEYARD — DATE:

IN A FIELD — DATE:

IN THE SKY — DATE:

ON A PICNIC — DATE:

UNDER THE STARS — DATE:

UNDER THE MOON — DATE:

IN THE SUNRAYS — DATE:

SET UP A PICNIC UNDER THE BIGGEST TREE IN A FIELD IN THE MIDDLE OF NOWHERE.
DO BRING A BLANKET, WINE, CHEESE + SEX OF COURSE!

UNDER A RAINBOW | DATE:

UNDER A PALM TREE | DATE:

UNDER A WEEPING WILLOW | DATE:

UNDER A PINE TREE | DATE:

IN THE RAIN | DATE:

ON THE GROUND | DATE:

IN A BACKYARD | DATE:

IN A FRONT YARD | DATE:

ON A DRIVEWAY | DATE:

ON THE BEACH | DATE:

OUTDOORS

ON A DECK   DATE:

ON A PATIO   DATE:

ON A PORCH   DATE:

IN A PARKING LOT   DATE:

IN THE SNOW   DATE:

IN A GARDEN   DATE:

IN A PARK   DATE:

IN A CORNFIELD   DATE:

ON A GOLF COURSE   DATE:

IN THE MOUNTAINS   DATE:

PAGE CHALLENGE   DATE:

JUST TAP IT IN! HAVE A MOONLIT RENDEZVOUS
ON THE GREEN OF THE NEAREST GOLF COURSE.
BE QUICK TO LOSE THOSE GOOFY GOLF PANTS!

BY THE CAMPFIRE   DATE:

SAND DUNE   DATE:

ON THE PATH   DATE:

OFF THE PATH   DATE:

SOCCER FIELD   DATE:

FOOTBALL FIELD   DATE:

BASEBALL FIELD   DATE:

TENNIS COURT   DATE:

SKATE PARK   DATE:

UNDER A VIADUCT   DATE:

48

WATER

WATER SLIDE	DATE:	
STEAM ROOM	DATE:	
SHOWER	DATE:	
SPRINLKER	DATE:	
BATH	DATE:	
OASIS	DATE:	
HOT TUB	DATE:	
GEYSER	DATE:	
POOL	DATE:	
FIRE HYDRANT	DATE:	

PAGE CHALLENGEDATE:

TIP: SEX IN "OPEN WATER" CAN BE CHALLENGING. WATER WILL WASH AWAY ANY NATURAL LUBE + CONDOMS TEND TO FALL OFF. BRING EXTRA!

STREAM DATE:

RIVER DATE:

POND DATE:

LAKE DATE:

GREAT LAKE DATE:

GULF DATE:

OCEAN DATE:

HOT SPRING DATE:

WATERFALL DATE:

WELL DATE:

PLACES IN THE WORLD

COUNTY YOU DO NOT LIVE IN) DATE:

ZIP CODE YOU DO NOT LIVE IN) DATE:

SOMEWHERE YOU'VE NEVER BEEN) DATE:

AN ALLEY) DATE:

A MARINA) DATE:

EQUATOR) DATE:

PRIME MERIDIAN) DATE:

UNITED STATES) DATE:

CANADA) DATE:

MEXICO) DATE:

PAGE CHALLENGE DATE:

EACH OF YOU IN DIFFERENT STATES, + NO! NOT OVER THE PHONE! THIS IS WHAT GPS WAS TRULY DESIGNED FOR!

LAS VEGAS DATE:

A DESERT DATE:

PACIFIC TIME ZONE DATE:

MOUNTAIN TIME ZONE DATE:

CENTRAL TIME ZONE DATE:

EASTERN TIME ZONE DATE:

EACH TIME ZONE DATE:

FOREIGN COUNTRY DATE:

NORTH POLE DATE:

SOUTH POLE DATE:

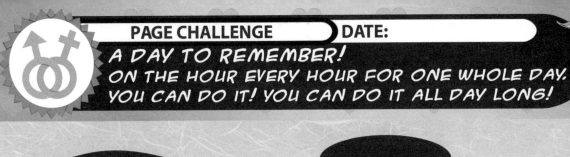

PAGE CHALLENGE
DATE:
TWICE A DAY, EVERY DAY FOR A WEEK STRAIGHT!
"WHEN IT'S NO LONGER A CHALLENGE, IT WILL BE THE NORM." - FORNY + KATE :)

SUNDAY	MONDAY	TUESDAY	WEDNESDAY	THURSDAY	FRIDAY	SATURDAY
	3x iN ONE DAY	4x iN ONE DAY	5x iN ONE DAY	6x iN ONE DAY	7x iN ONE DAY	8x iN ONE DAY
2x iN ONE DAY		3 DAYS iN A ROW			2 DAYS iN A ROW	
2 DAYS iN A ROW				3 DAYS iN A ROW		
4 DAYS iN A ROW						
5 DAYS iN A ROW						

DATES

YOUR BIRTHDAY DATE:

YOUR LOVER'S BIRTHDAY DATE:

CHRISTMAS DATE:

HANUKKAH DATE:

CHRISTMAKUH DATE:

ANY HOLIDAY DATE:

HALLOWEEN DATE:

THANKSGIVING DATE:

NEW YEAR'S EVE DATE:

NEW YEAR'S DAY DATE:

INDEPENDENCE DAY   DATE:

MOTHERS DAY   DATE:

FATHERS DAY   DATE:

VALENTINES DAY   DATE:

LUNAR ECLIPSE   DATE:

SOLAR ECLIPSE   DATE:

FULL MOON   DATE:

HALF MOON   DATE:

QUARTER MOON   DATE:

DAYLIGHT SAVINGS (SPRING)   DATE:

DATES

DAYLIGHT SAVINGS (FALL) | DATE:

29 FEBRUARY 29TH | DATE:

$ BLACK FRIDAY | DATE:

LABOR DAY | DATE:

MEMORIAL DAY | DATE:

GROUNDHOG DAY | DATE:

CANADA DAY | DATE:

CINCO DE MAYO | DATE:

FRIDAY THE 13TH | DATE:

NO PANTS DAY | DATE:

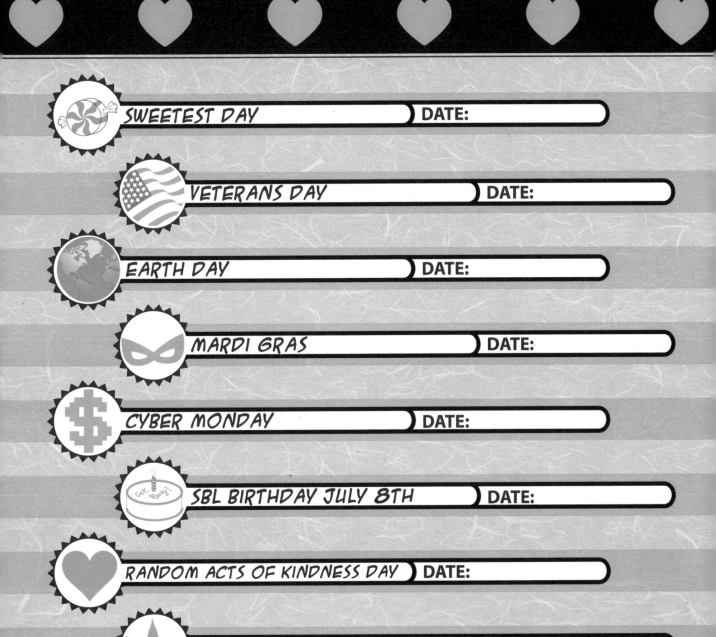

SWEETEST DAY DATE:

VETERANS DAY DATE:

EARTH DAY DATE:

MARDI GRAS DATE:

CYBER MONDAY DATE:

SBL BIRTHDAY JULY 8TH DATE:

RANDOM ACTS OF KINDNESS DAY DATE:

420 DATE:

MISCHIEF NIGHT DATE:

INTERNATIONAL BEER DAY DATE:

ANNIVERSARIES

Share your anniversary exploits & gifts here!

5 YEAR ANNIVERSARY

10 YEAR ANNIVERSARY

15 YEAR ANNIVERSARY

20 YEAR ANNIVERSARY

25 YEAR ANNIVERSARY

PAGE CHALLENGE **DATE:**

TIP: DON'T JUST MAKE THIS DAY A SPECIAL DAY.
THE DAYS IN BETWEEN ARE SPECIAL TOO.
CHERISH THESE DAYS FOR ALL DAYS TO CUM!

 30 YEAR ANNIVERSARY

 35 YEAR ANNIVERSARY

 40 YEAR ANNIVERSARY

 45 YEAR ANNIVERSARY

 50 YEAR ANNIVERSARY

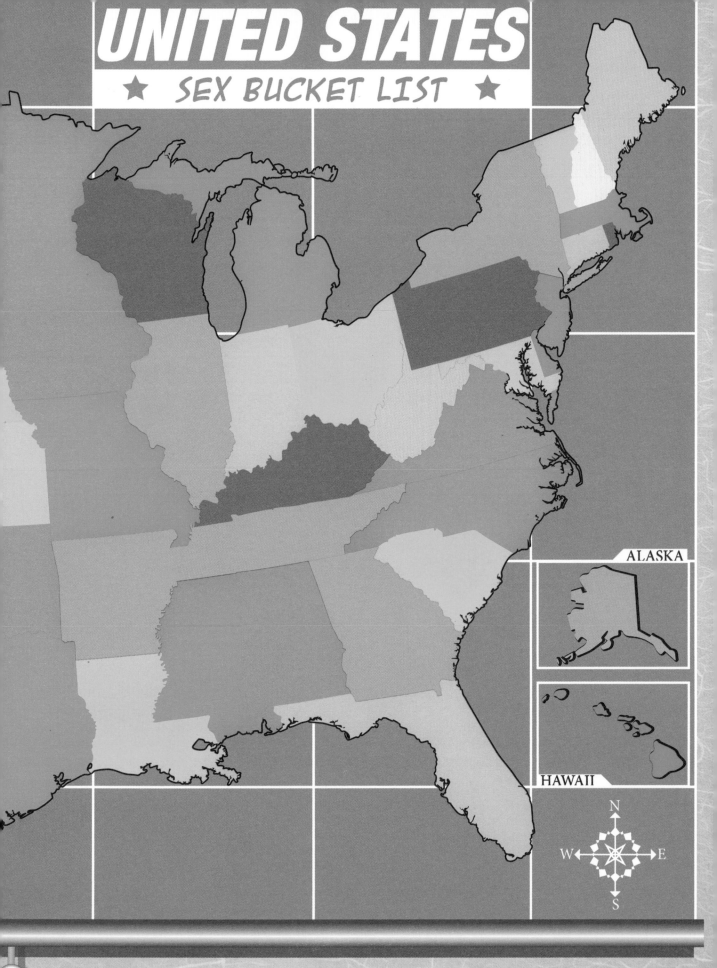

UNITED STATES
★ SEX BUCKET LIST ★

ALASKA

HAWAII

CONTINENTS

NORTH
AMERICA

SOUTH
AMERICA

ANTARCTICA

MARK YOUR APPROXIMATE TRAVEL ROUTE
FROM ONE CONTINENT TO ANOTHER.

EUROPE

ASIA

AFRICA

AUSTRALIA

N

W   E

S

WONDERS OF THE WORLD

GREAT WALL OF CHINA DATE:

GALAPAGOS ISLANDS DATE:

MACHU PICCHU DATE:

CHICHEN ITZA DATE:

ROMAN COLOSSEUM DATE:

TAJ MAJAL DATE:

PETRA DATE:

GRAND CANYON DATE:

THE GREAT BARRIER REEF DATE:

VICTORIA FALLS DATE:

PAGE CHALLENGE | DATE:

TIP: WE MAY NOT BE ABLE TO VISIT ALL THESE PLACES IN A LIFETIME, BUT WE CAN BE CREATIVE, USE OUR IMAGINATIONS + ROLE-PLAY!

MT. EVEREST | DATE:

NORTHERN LIGHTS | DATE:

PARICUTIN VOLCANO | DATE:

AMAZON RAINFOREST | DATE:

REDWOOD NATIONAL PARK | DATE:

STONEHENGE | DATE:

GREAT PYRAMID OF GIZA | DATE:

HANGING GARDENS OF BABYLON | DATE:

TEMPLE OF ARTEMIS AT EPHESUS | DATE:

LIGHTHOUSE OF ALEXANDRIA | DATE:

» PERSONALS

CREATE

WRITE & DRAW
YOUR OWN SEX BUCKET LIST ITEMS!

DATE: _____

DATE: _____

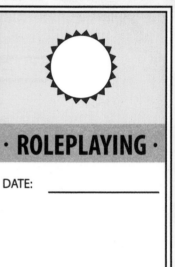

· ROLEPLAYING ·

DATE: _____

MISSING

AWARDS · HONORS

DATE: _____

TEXT ME @ _____ FOR A GOOD TIME =)
1 :)
SEND ME A PIC OF YOU _____
1 :)

DATE: _____

DATE: _____

INTERESTS

FREE

DATE: _____

DATE: _____

OTHER

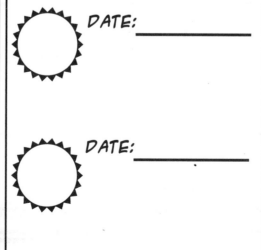

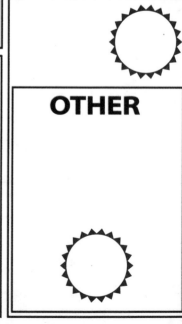

PERSONALS

CREATE

WRITE & DRAW
YOUR OWN SEX BUCKET LIST ITEMS!

DATE: _____

DATE: _____

DATE: _____

HELP WANTED

DATE: _____

FREE

DATE: _____

OTHER

BUCKET LIST ®

"Get Busy, Gettin' Busy," "why not," and "no only means no when the safe word follows," are just a few things Michael Lucente, author and creator of **The Sex Bucket List®** might say if sex is a question. Having not been a romance writer or sexual therapist, it's easy to question Michael's writing abilities and this book. He once said, "**TSBL** is not a literary masterpiece. Although, it is a masterpiece. This is not a book for reading. It's a book for doing. Name anything else that challenges couples to be intimate in over 600 situations and provides a fun way for them to reflect back on the wild times. Before **TSBL** no one had ever whispered in my ear, "Let's get dirty in a teepee," and I never asked my lover to "build an igloo out of snow with me and then melt it from the inside."

Married and living together in the suburbs of Chicago, Michael and Lisa share and do just about everything together: cooking, cleaning, pet detail, couch surfing, exercising, going out, bills, you know, life. But what's the one thing they know they do more than just about everyone else? Sex, sex, sex! What did you expect, needlepoint?

Lisa and I went on a trip to Montana and while we have tons of pictures from the trip, what really lights up our memories the most is seeing that kiss stamp next to "in the mountains" in our copy of **The Sex Bucket List®**. All the memories, all the feelings, each of our favorite moments come rushing to us when we look through our copy. Not just the moments we ripped off our clothes and ravished each other's bodies, but of all the fun we had in the mountains each day we spent together there. I hope that my book can help you to create your own memories, moments, and feelings from your shared lives as well.

THANKS AGAIN AND AS ALWAYS...
GET BUSY, GETTIN' BUSY!
MICHAEL LUCENTE